OLD MacDONALD
HAD ★A★ TRUCK

For my son, Connor, whose love for trucks inspired this book. —S. G.

To my father, who spent his whole life among big trucks and even
let me take the wheel that one time. —E. K.

★

ISBN 978-1-338-11208-5

12 11 10 9 8 7 6 5 4 3 2   16 17 18 19 20 21

Printed in the U.S.A.   40

First Scholastic printing, September 2016

Book design by Ryan Hayes
Typeset in Bandoliers, Monstro Solid, and Populaire
The illustrations in this book were rendered in pencil and gouache, and composited digitally.

OLD MacDONALD HAD A TRUCK

By Steve Goetz   Illustrated by Eda Kaban

SCHOLASTIC INC.

Old MacDonald had a farm
E-I-E-I-O.

And on that farm he had an . . .

E - I - E - I - O.
With a **DIG DIG** here and a **DIG DIG** there,
here a **DIG**, there a **DIG**, everywhere a **DIG DIG**.

Old MacDonald had a farm
E - I - E - I - O.

And on that farm he had a . . .

With a **SCOOOP SCOOP** here and a **SCOOOP SCOOP** there, here a **SCOOP**, there a **SCOOP**, everywhere a **SCOOOP SCOOP**.

Old MacDonald had a farm
E-I-E-I-O.

And on that farm he had a . . .

With a **PUUUSH PUSH** here
and a **PUUUSH PUSH** there,
here a **PUSH**, there a **PUSH**,
everywhere a **PUUUSH PUSH**.

E-I-E-I-

MOW

Old MacDonald had a farm
E - I - E - I - O.

And on that farm he had a . . .

With a SCRAPE RAKE here
and a RAKE SCRAPE there,
here a SCRAPE, there a RAKE,
everywhere a SCRAPE RAKE.

And on that farm he had a . . .

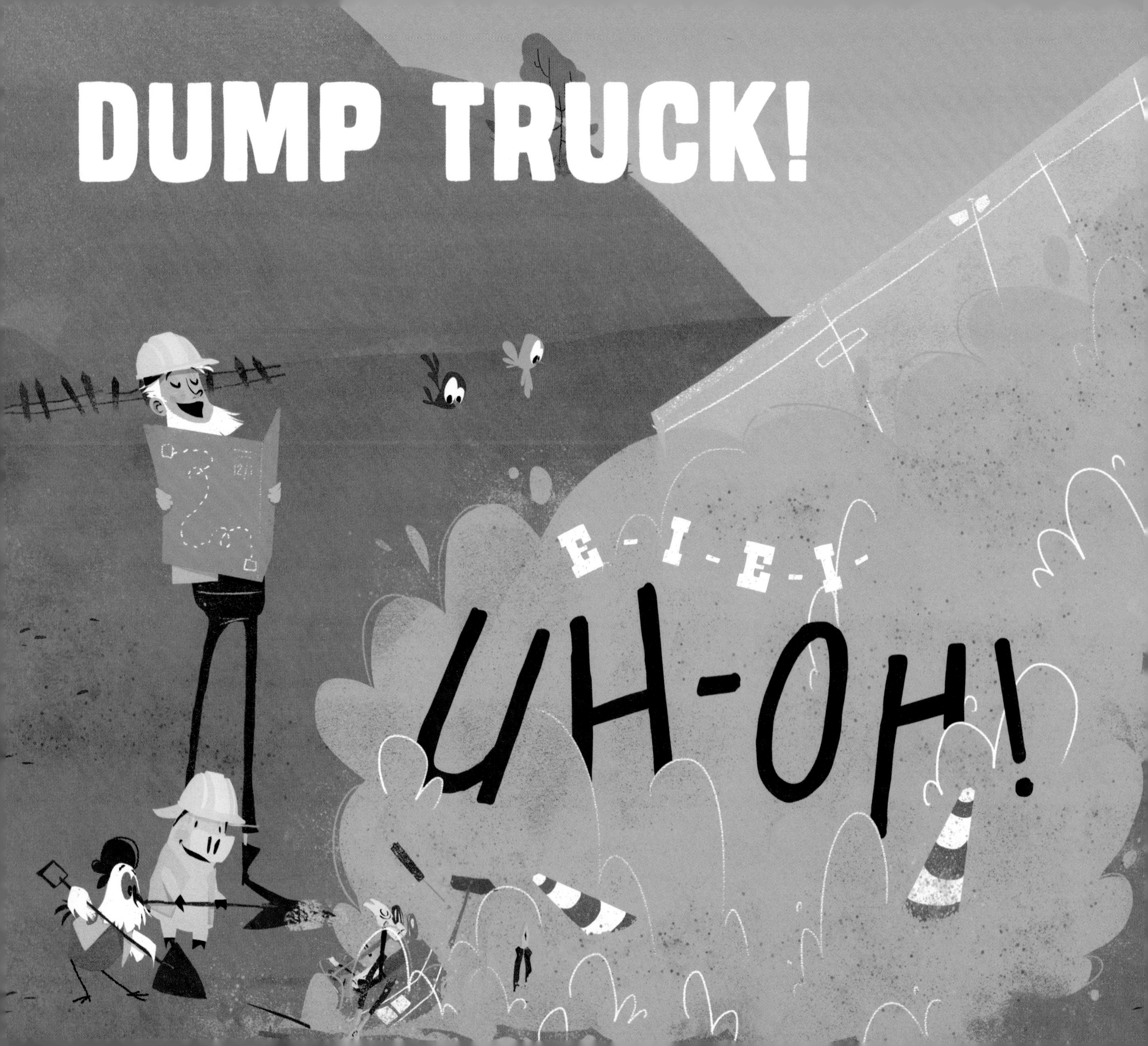
DUMP TRUCK!
E-I-E-I-
UH-OH!

With a **DUMP THUMP** here
and a **DUMP THUMP** there,
here a **DUMP**, there a **THUMP**,
everywhere a **DUMP THUMP**.

Old MacDonald had a farm
E - I - E - I - O.

And on that farm he had a . . .

STEAMROLLER!

With a **SQUISH SMASH** here and a **SQUISH SMASH** there,
here a **SQUISH**, there a **SMASH**, everywhere a **SQUISH SMASH**.

Old MacDonald had a farm
E-I-E-I-O.

And on that farm he had a . . .

CEMENT MIXER!

E-I-E-I-

FLOW

With a SPIN WHIRL here
and a SPIN WHIRL there,
here a SPIN, there a WHIRL,
everywhere a SPIN WHIRL.

MAC

Old MacDonald had a farm
E - I - E - I - O.

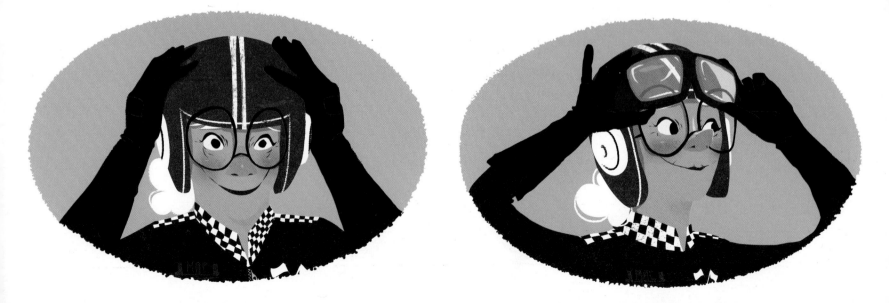

And on that farm he had a . . .